JOHN THOMPSON'S
EASIEST PIANO COUR

FIRST ABBA HITS

This collection of popular ABBA songs is intended as supplementary material for those working through **John Thompson's Easiest Piano Course** Parts 2–4. The pieces may also be used for sight reading practice by more advanced students.

Dynamics and phrasing have been deliberately omitted from the earlier pieces, since they are not introduced until Part 3 of the Easiest Piano Course, and initially the student's attention should be focused on playing notes and rhythms accurately. Outline fingering has been included, and in general the hand is assumed to remain in a five-finger position until a new fingering indicates a position shift. The fingering should suit most hands, although logical alternatives are always possible.

Super Trouper

Words & Music by Benny Andersson & Björn Ulvaeus

Steadily

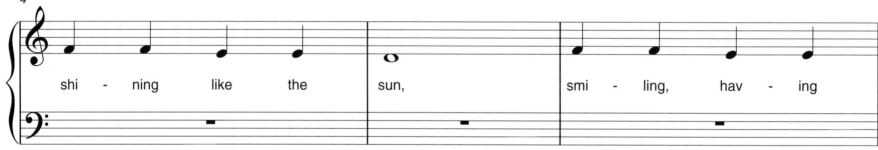

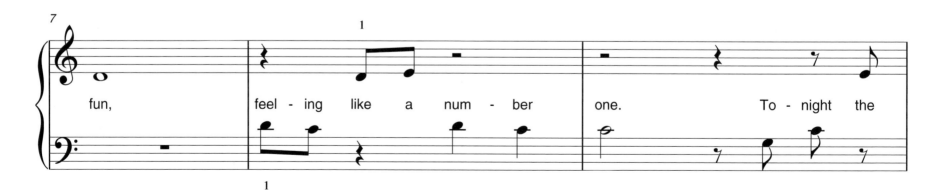

© Copyright 1980 Union Songs AB, Sweden.
Bocu Music Limited for Great Britain and the Republic Of Ireland.
All Rights Reserved. International Copyright Secured.

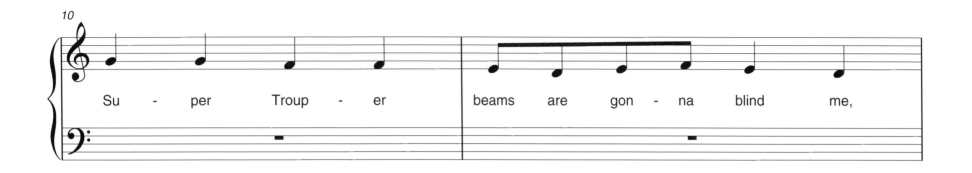

Su - per Troup - er beams are gon - na blind me,

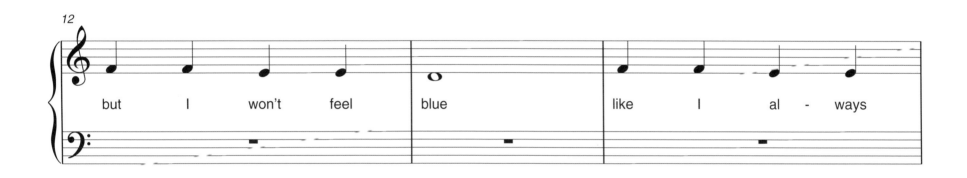

but I won't feel blue like I al - ways

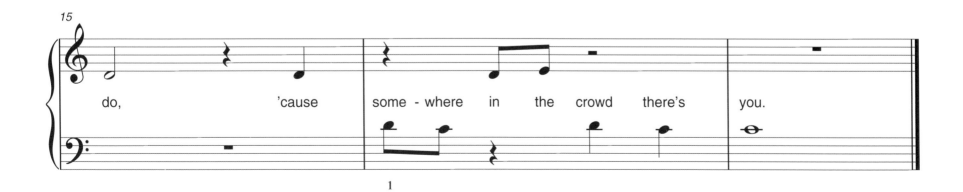

do, 'cause some - where in the crowd there's you.

Knowing Me, Knowing You

Words & Music by Benny Andersson, Stig Anderson & Björn Ulvaeus

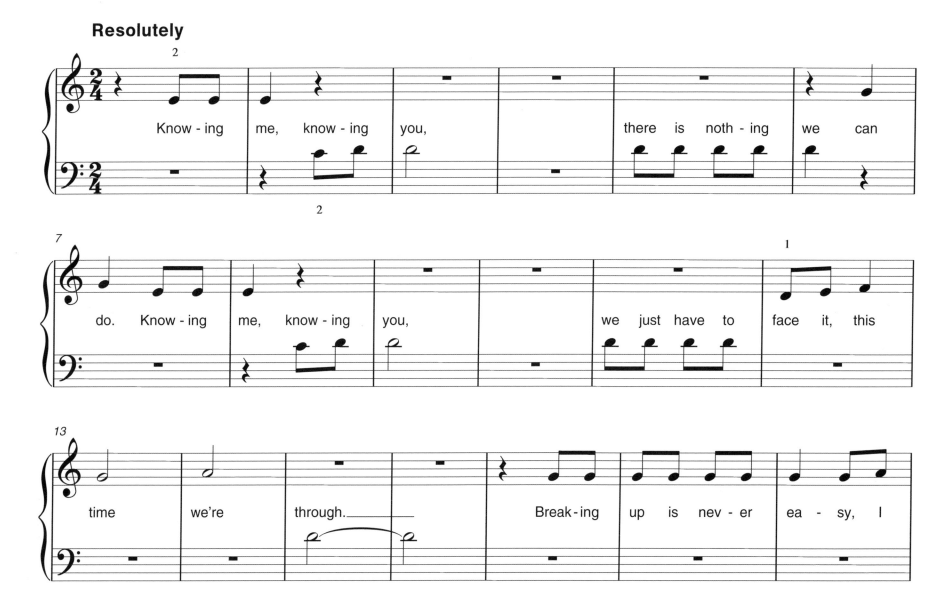

© Copyright 1976 Union Songs AB, Sweden.
Bocu Music Limited for Great Britain and the Republic Of Ireland.
All Rights Reserved. International Copyright Secured.

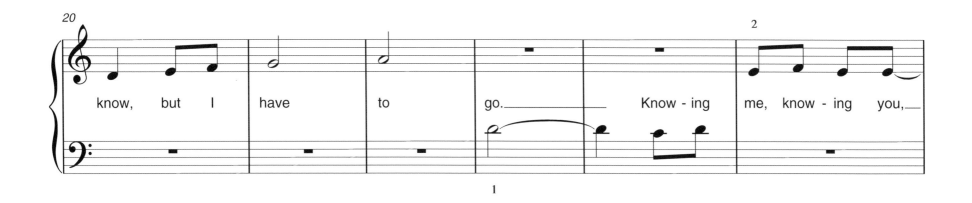

know, but I   have   to   go.   Know - ing   me,   know - ing   you,

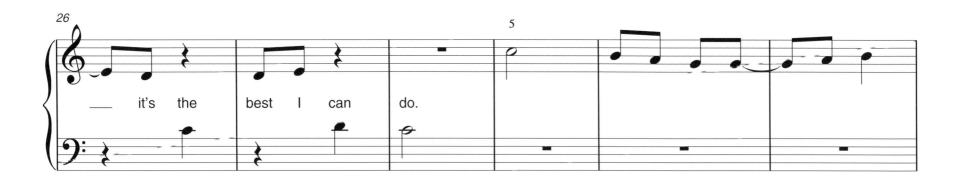

___ it's   the   best   I   can   do.

Mamma Mia

Words & Music by Benny Andersson, Stig Anderson & Björn Ulvaeus

Energetically

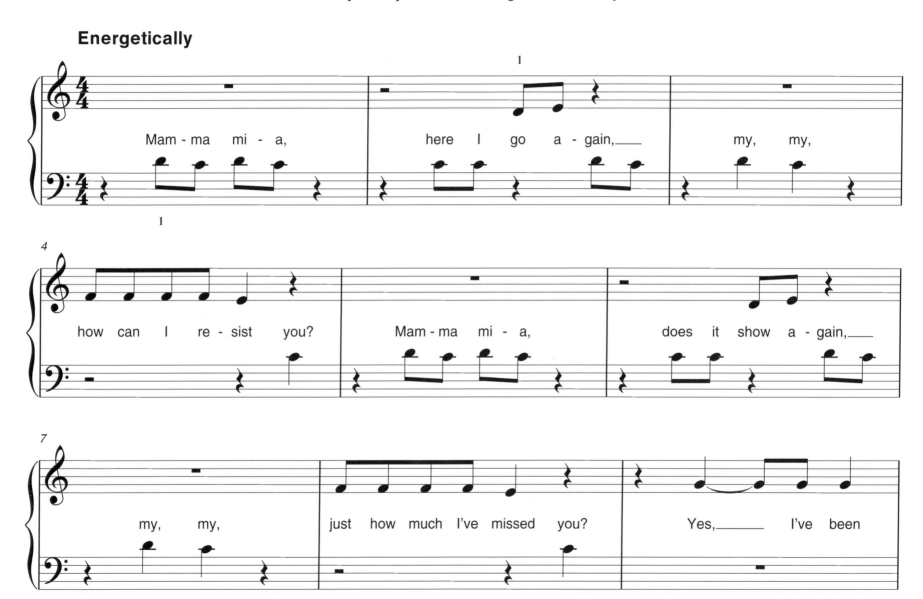

© Copyright 1975 Union Songs AB, Sweden.
Bocu Music Limited for Great Britain and the Republic Of Ireland.
All Rights Reserved. International Copyright Secured.

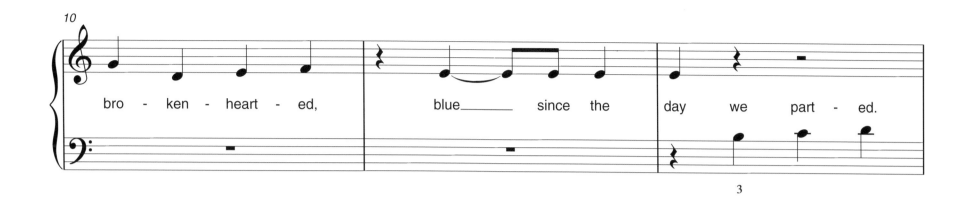

broken - ken - heart - ed, blue_____ since the day we part - ed.

Why, why did I ev - er let you go?_____ Mam - ma mi - a,

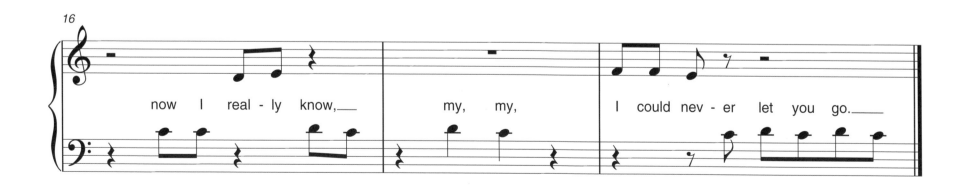

now I real - ly know,___ my, my, I could nev - er let you go.___

Lay All Your Love On Me

Words & Music by Benny Andersson & Björn Ulvaeus

With movement

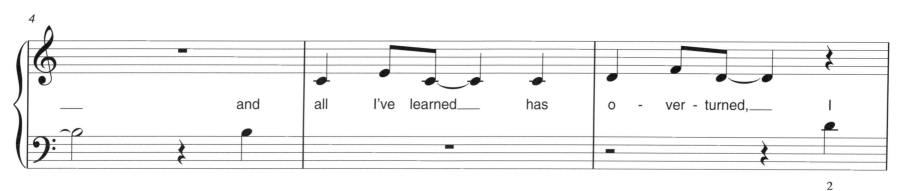

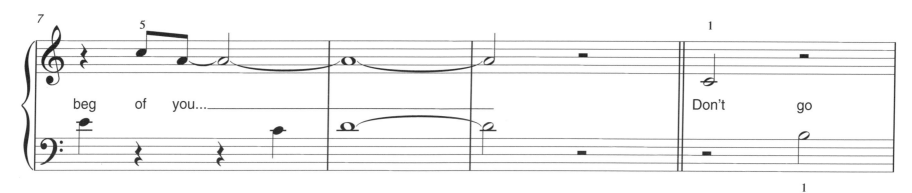

© Copyright 1980 Union Songs AB, Sweden.
Bocu Music Limited for Great Britain and the Republic Of Ireland.
All Rights Reserved. International Copyright Secured.

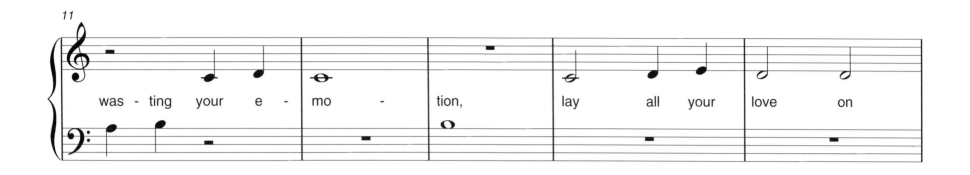

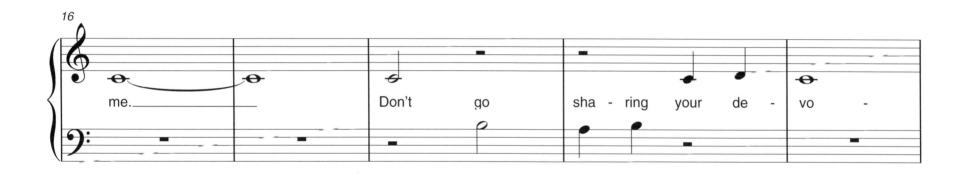

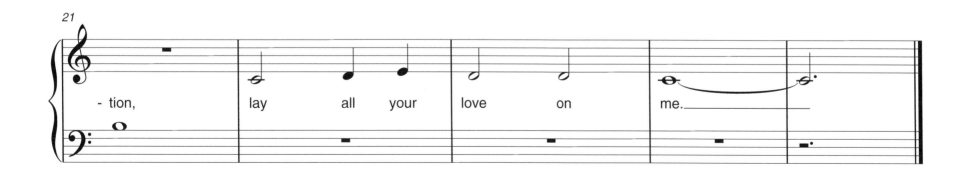

Honey Honey

Words & Music by Benny Andersson, Stig Anderson & Björn Ulvaeus

© Copyright 1974 Union Songs AB, Sweden.
Bocu Music Limited for Great Britain and the Republic Of Ireland.
All Rights Reserved. International Copyright Secured.

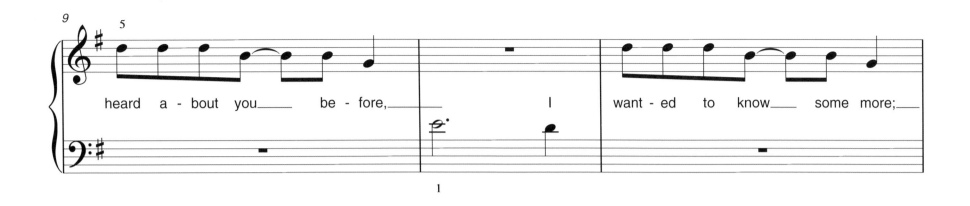

heard a - bout you___ be - fore,___ I want - ed to know___ some more;___

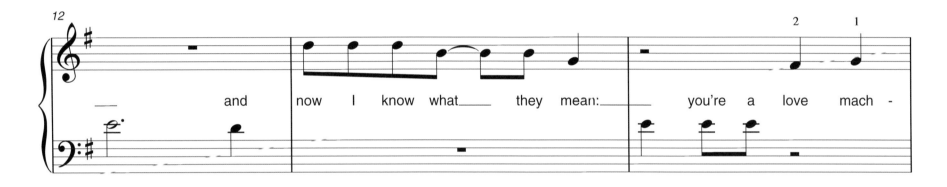

___ and now I know what___ they mean:___ you're a love mach -

-ine. Oh, you make me diz - zy! Hon - ey, hon - ey!

Fernando

Words & Music by Benny Andersson, Björn Ulvaeus & Stig Anderson

Energetically

© Copyright 1976 Union Songs AB, Sweden.
Bocu Music Limited for Great Britain and the Republic Of Ireland.
All Rights Reserved. International Copyright Secured.

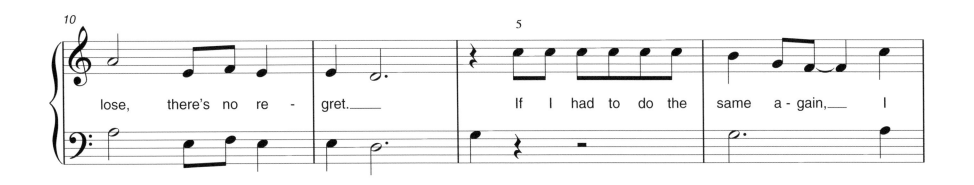

Gimme! Gimme! Gimme! (A Man After Midnight)

Words & Music by Benny Andersson & Björn Ulvaeus

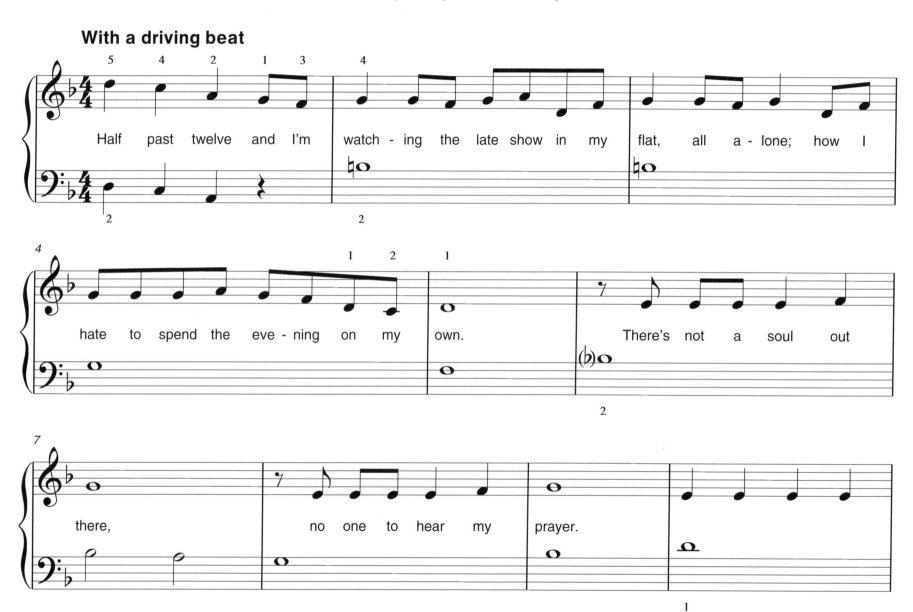

© Copyright 1979 Union Songs AB, Sweden.
Bocu Music Limited for Great Britain and the Republic Of Ireland.
All Rights Reserved. International Copyright Secured.

Gim - me, gim - me, gim - me a   man af - ter mid – night.

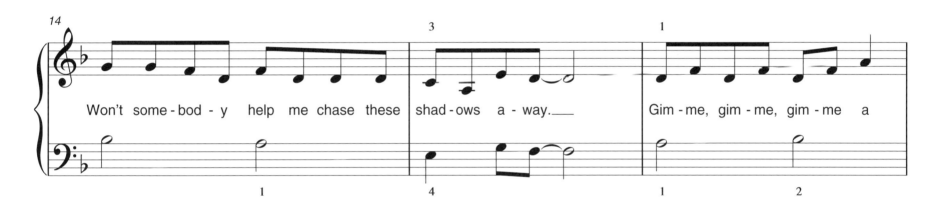

Won't some - bod - y help me chase these   shad - ows a - way.___   Gim - me, gim - me, gim - me a

man af - ter mid – night.   Take me through the dark - ness to the   break of the day.___

Money, Money, Money

Words & Music by Benny Andersson & Björn Ulvaeus

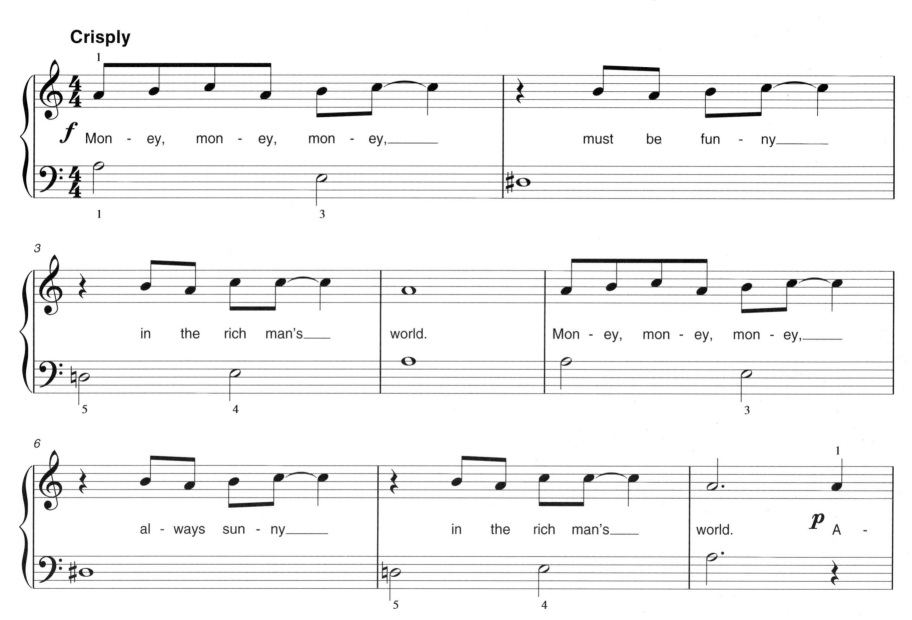

© Copyright 1976 Union Songs AB, Sweden.
Bocu Music Limited for Great Britain and the Republic Of Ireland.
All Rights Reserved. International Copyright Secured.

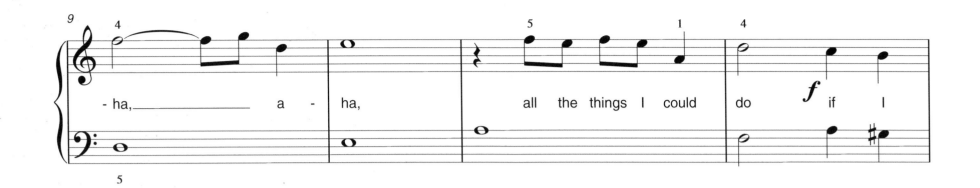

-ha,_____ a - ha,   all the things I could do   *f* if I

had a lit - tle mon - ey;___   it's a rich man's___ world.

p It's a rich man's___ world.

Waterloo

Words & Music by Benny Andersson, Stig Anderson & Björn Ulvaeus

© Copyright 1974 Union Songs AB, Sweden.
Bocu Music Limited for Great Britain and the Republic Of Ireland.
All Rights Reserved. International Copyright Secured.

I Have A Dream

Words & Music by Benny Andersson & Björn Ulvaeus

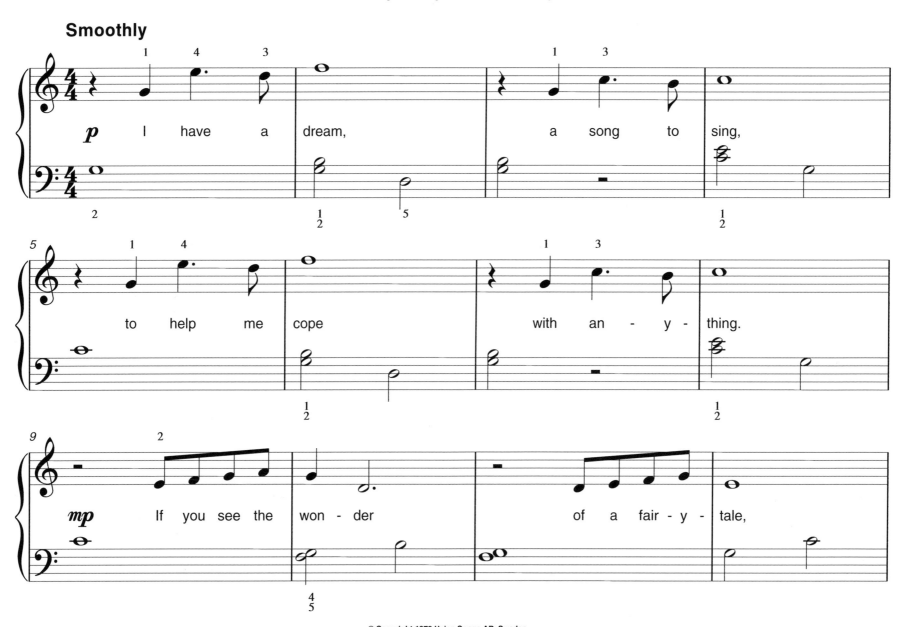

© Copyright 1979 Union Songs AB, Sweden.
Bocu Music Limited for Great Britain and the Republic Of Ireland.
All Rights Reserved. International Copyright Secured.

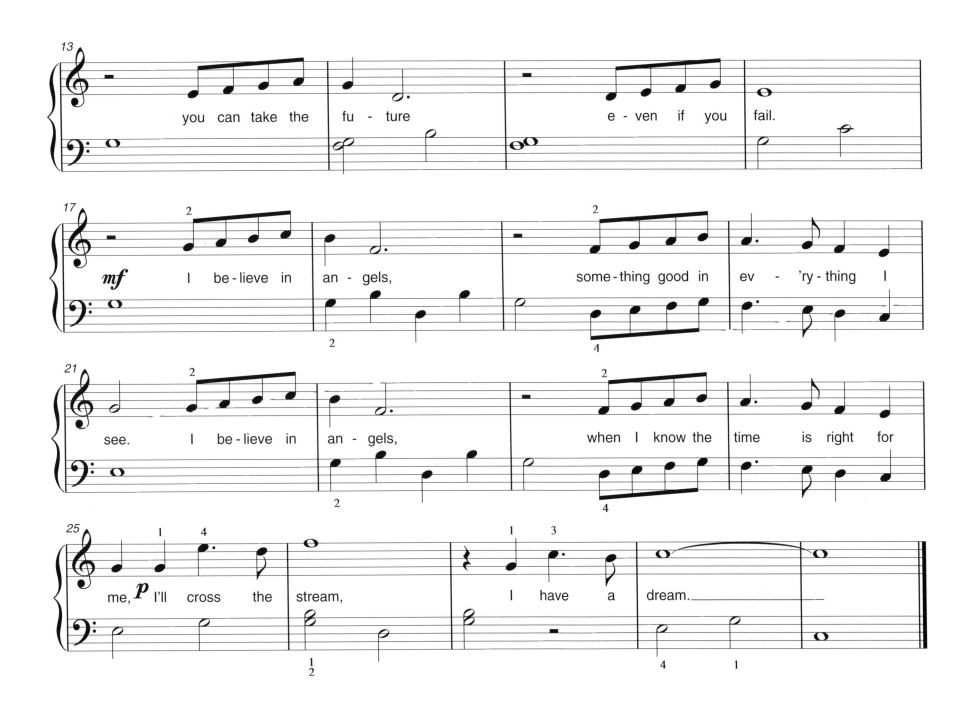

The Winner Takes It All

Words & Music by Benny Andersson & Björn Ulvaeus

© Copyright 1980 Union Songs AB, Sweden.
Bocu Music Limited for Great Britain and the Republic Of Ireland.
All Rights Reserved. International Copyright Secured.

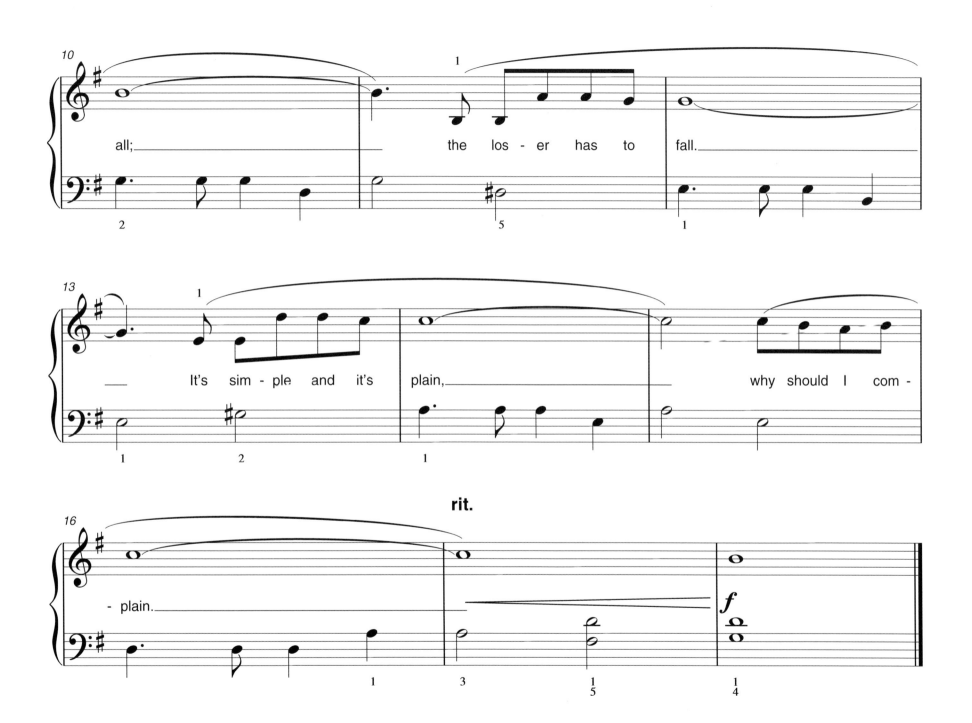

all;_____ the los - er has to fall._____

____ It's sim - ple and it's plain,_____ why should I com -

rit.

- plain._____

f

Voulez-Vous

Words & Music by Benny Andersson & Björn Ulvaeus

With a driving beat

© Copyright 1979 Union Songs AB, Sweden.
Bocu Music Limited for Great Britain and the Republic Of Ireland.
All Rights Reserved. International Copyright Secured.

you know what to do,_____ la ques - tion c'est voul - ez -

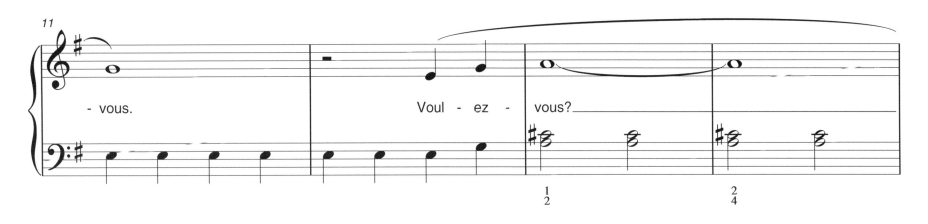

- vous. Voul - ez - vous?_____

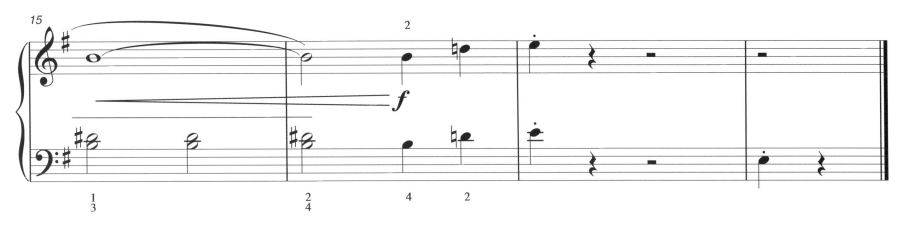

Chiquitita

Words & Music by Benny Andersson & Björn Ulvaeus

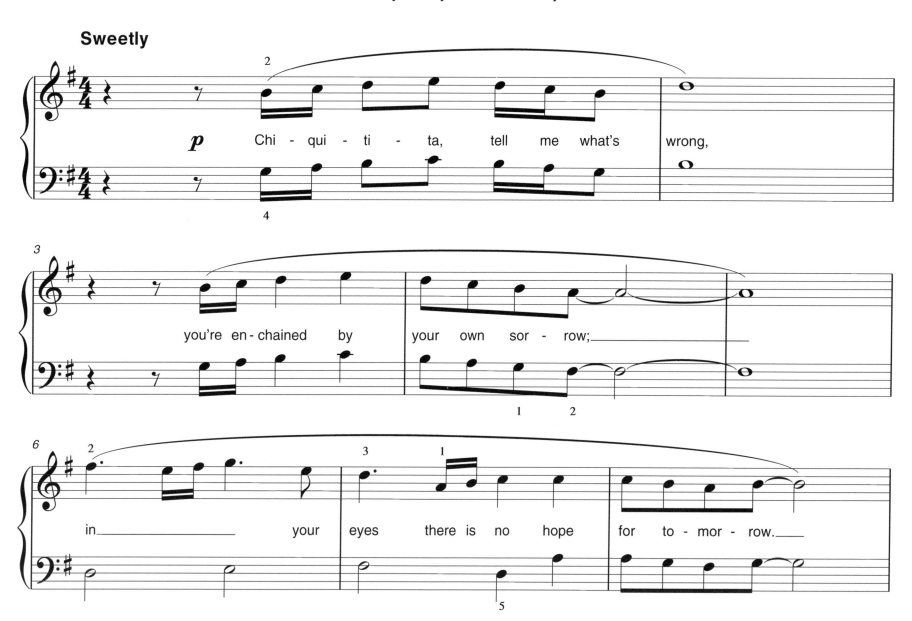

© Copyright 1979 Union Songs AB, Sweden.
Bocu Music Limited for Great Britain and the Republic Of Ireland.
All Rights Reserved. International Copyright Secured.

Dancing Queen

Words & Music by Benny Andersson, Stig Anderson & Björn Ulvaeus

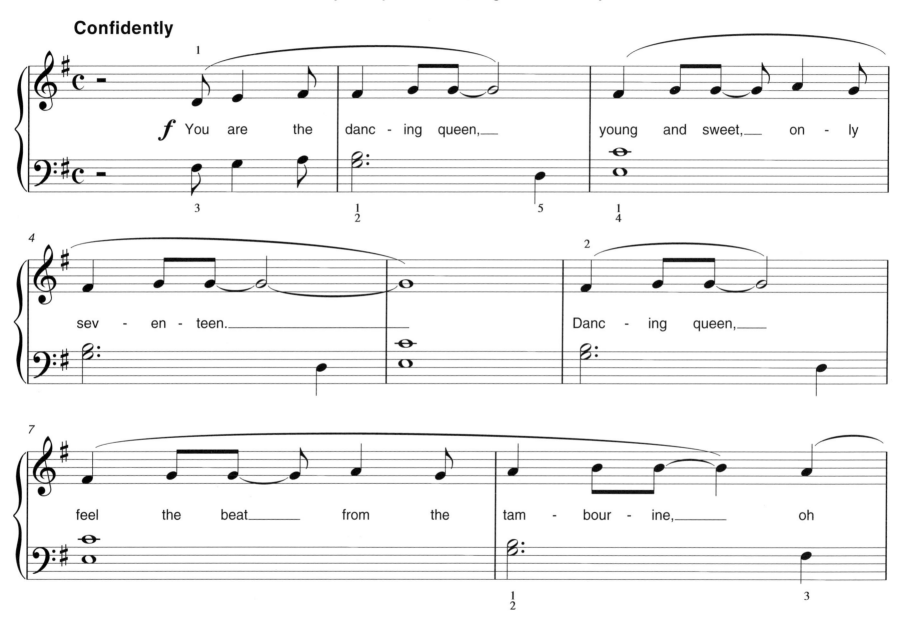

© Copyright 1976 Union Songs AB, Sweden.
Bocu Music Limited for Great Britain and the Republic Of Ireland.
All Rights Reserved. International Copyright Secured.

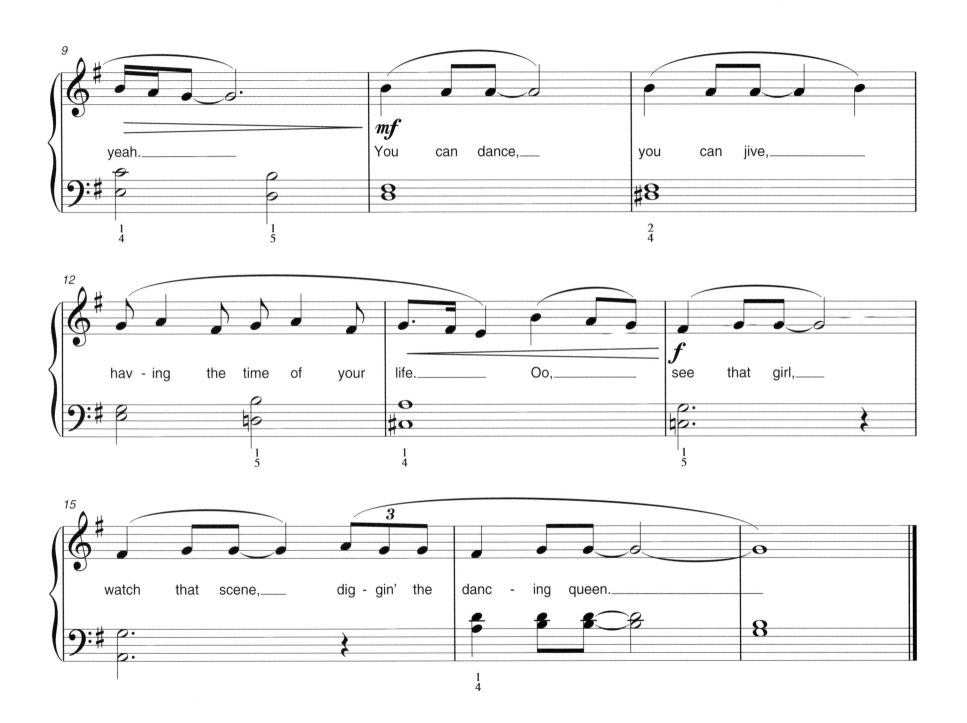

Thank You For The Music

Words & Music by Benny Andersson & Björn Ulvaeus

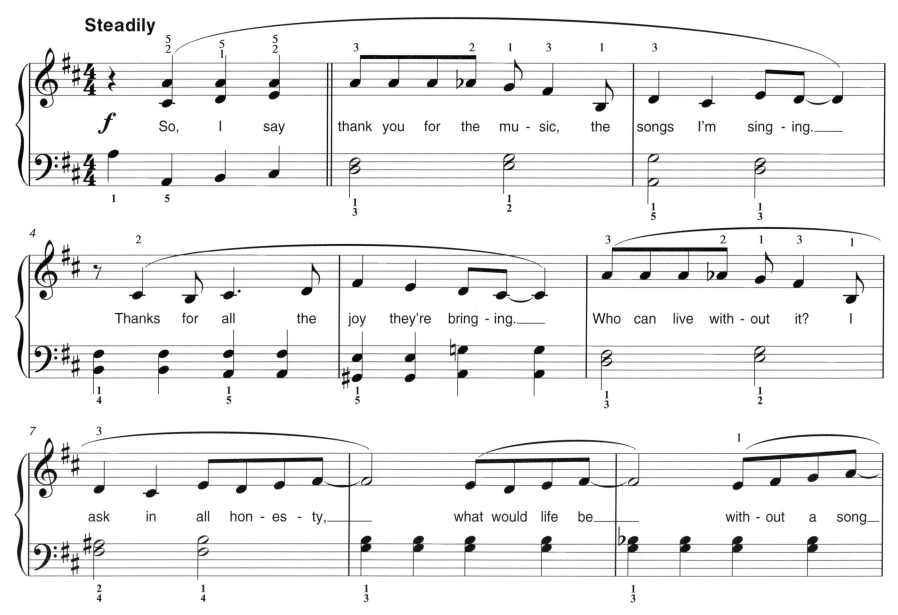

© Copyright 1977 Union Songs AB, Sweden.
Bocu Music Limited for Great Britain and the Republic Of Ireland.
All Rights Reserved. International Copyright Secured.

© Copyright 2013 The Willis Music Company
Florence, Kentucky, USA. All Rights Reserved.

Exclusive Distributors:
Music Sales Limited
Newmarket Road, Bury St Edmunds, Suffolk IP33 3YB, UK.
Music Sales Pty Limited
Units 3-4, 17 Willfox Street, Condell Park, NSW 2200, Australia.

Order No. WMR101277
ISBN: 978-1-78038-913-4

Unauthorised reproduction of any part of this publication by any means
including photocopying is an infringement of copyright.

Arranged by Christopher Hussey.
Arrangements and engravings supplied by Camden Music Services.
Edited by Sam Lung.

Printed in the EU.